THE WORLD OF DINOSAURS
ACTIVITY BOOK

All this inside...

SPOT IT

Can you find the fossil hidden on this page?

Published 2023. Little Brother Books Ltd, Ground Floor, 23 Southernhay East, Exeter, Devon EX1 1QL
books@littlebrotherbooks.co.uk | www.littlebrotherbooks.co.uk
Printed in the United Kingdom.

LB BOOKS

BRAIN BOX

For a dinosaur, Tyrannosaurus must have been pretty smart – its brain was twice the size of other giant meat-eaters.

KILLER TEETH

Tyrannosaurus had 60 sharp teeth inside its mighty jaws. These deadly gnashers were strong enough to crunch through bone. **Awesome!**

SUPER SPEED

It may have been big but fearsome Tyrannosaurus was fast on its feet. Only the quickest of dinosaurs would have been able to outrun a hungry T-rex.

DID YOU KNOW?
Tyrannosaurus could swallow a small dinosaur whole. **Gulp!**

MEET THE DINOS

TYRANNOSAURUS

The fierce dinosaur king.

DINO STATS

NAME	TYRANNOSAURUS (TYE-**RAN**-OH-**SORE**-US)
MEANING	TYRANT LIZARD
FOOD	MEAT
SIZE	12M

DINO RATING

Give this dinosaur scores out of 10.

KILLER-RATING

/10

SUPER-SIZE

/10

BIG-BITE

/10

DINO FOOTPRINTS

How many **Tyrannosaurus** footprints can you count?

IT'S A FACT!

Tyrannosaurus's deadly bite was three times as powerful as a lion's. Wow!

Answers on pages 48.

T-REX TRAIL

Can you guide this fearsome Tyrannosaurus along the trail, completing the activities as you go?

START

1

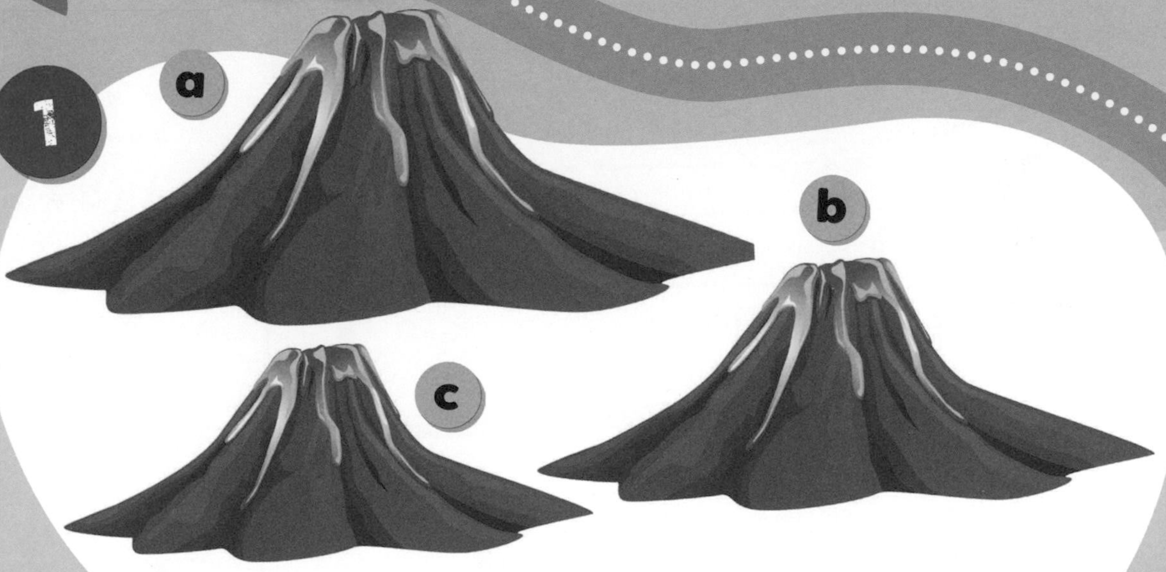

a

b

c

Circle the biggest volcano.

2

Colour 4 eggs green and 3 eggs blue.

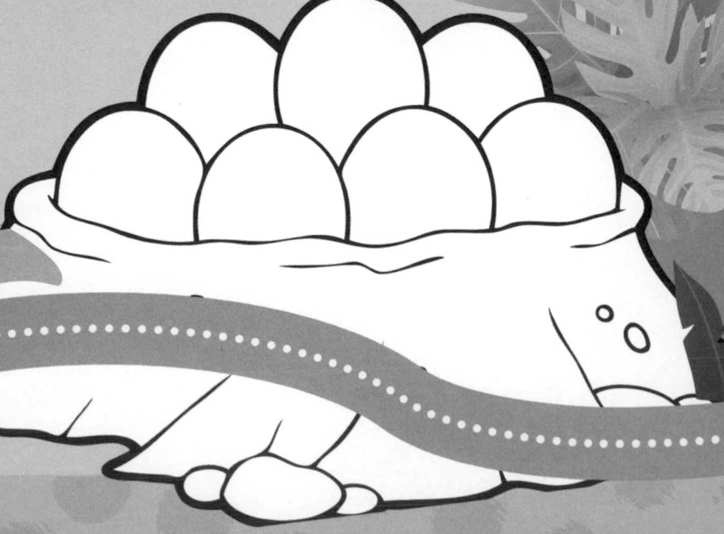

4 Tick who is hiding behind the boulders.

3 Find the fossil hidden somewhere on these pages.

5 Trace the footprints to the finish, then colour them in.

FINISH

Answers on pages 48.

UNUSUAL DINO

Parasaurolophus was a strange looking dinosaur with a fancy head crest and unusually shaped tail. Its wide, flat mouth looked a bit like a duck's bill. **Quack quack!**

IT'S A FACT!

Parasaurolophus had hundreds of tiny teeth.

MAKING MUSIC

Parasaurolophus could make a sound like a trumpet with its head crest. This may have been how they communicated with other dinosaurs. **Cool!**

STRONG LEGS

Plant-eating Parasaurolophus could walk on two or four legs. It's back legs were super strong so it could stand to munch high-up leaves.

DID YOU KNOW?

Parasaurolophus lived and travelled in large herds.

PARASAUROLOPHUS

The one that could make music.

DINO RATING

Give this dinosaur scores out of 10.

FIERCE-FACTOR

/10

MUSICAL TALENT

/10

BITE SCORE

/10

DINO STATS

NAME
PARASAUROLOPHUS (PA-RA-SAW-**ROL**-OFF-US)

MEANING
NEAR CRESTED LIZARD

FOOD
PLANTS

SIZE
12M

FINDING FOOD

Follow the trails to see which hungry **Parasaurolophus** will reach the leaves first.

a

b

c

MYTH BUSTER

Not everything you think you know about dinosaurs is true! Read on to sort the facts from the fiction.

ALL DINOSAURS WERE HUGE.

FALSE

Although lots of dinosaurs were gigantic, the world's first dinosaurs were all small.

ALL DINOSAURS HATCHED FROM EGGS.

TRUE

Even the dinosaurs that grew up to be huge started life as an egg.

ALL DINOSAURS HAD SHARP TEETH

FALSE

Some dinos, like Oviraptor, were toothless.

PTERODACTYL WAS A DINOSAUR.

FALSE

Pterodactyl was a flying reptile that lived during the same time period as the dinosaurs.

ALL DINOSAURS HAD SCALES.

FALSE

Scientists used to think this but they now know that lots of dinosaurs had feathers instead.

DINOSAURS COULDNT FLY.

TRUE

Some dinosaurs, like Microraptor, could glide but no dinosaur could fly.

SOME DINOSAURS DIDN'T HAVE TAILS.

FALSE

All dinosaurs had tails to help them balance.

RELATIVES OF THE DINOSAURS STILL LIVE TODAY.

TRUE

The birds that live on earth today are related to the dinosaurs.

STANDING TALL

Although images of Diplodocus often show the dino with its head held high, some scientists think it wouldn't have been able to do this. They believe its heart couldn't have pumped blood all the way up its long neck.

NOISY TAIL

Diplodocus could make a loud, booming sound with its tail. It used it like a whip to make attackers back off. **Cool!**

DINO DIET

Plant-eating Diplodocus swallowed stones with its food – it made it easier to digest the tough plants it ate. **Urgh!**

IT'S A FACT!
Diplodocus's enormous tail had 80 backbones.

MEET THE DINOS

DIPLODOCUS

One of the longest dinosaurs ever.

DINO STATS

NAME
DIPLODOCUS (**DIP**-LOW-**DOCK**-US)

MEANING
DOUBLE BEAM

FOOD
PLANTS

SIZE
27M

DINO RATING

Give this dinosaur scores out of 10.

FIERCE-FACTOR

/10

SUPER-SIZE

/10

TAIL RATING

/10

DINO CLOSE-UPS

Which of these body parts doesn't belong to Diplodocus?

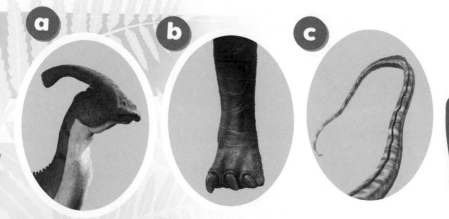

a
b
c

DID YOU KNOW?
A cast of a Diplodocus skeleton was on display in London's Natural History Museum for over 100 years.

11

SHADOW MATCH

Only one of these shadows matches the Ankylosaurus picture exactly. Can you spot which one?

a

b

c

d

Answers on pages 48.

FOSSIL FUN

This Stegosaurus wants to get back to its eggs. Can you use the key to follow the fossil path and lead it home?

KEY

START →

FINISH

BONY BACK PLATES

Stegosaurus had eye-catching back plates which could have been used to regulate the dinosaur's temperature or to attract mates.

DINNER TIME

Plant-eating Stegosaurus didn't have any teeth so it used its sharp beak to nip at plants. It walked on four legs so wouldn't have been able to reach high up leaves.

DID YOU KNOW?
Stegosaurus's back plates may have flashed red to warn off attackers. Awesome!

IT'S A FACT!
Stegosaurus had a tiny brain about the size of a walnut.

DANGEROUS TAIL

Stegosaurus had a built-in weapon – it's spiky tail. The strong dino swung it from side-to-side to fend off attackers.

STEGOSAURUS

The big dinosaur with a small brain.

DINO STATS

NAME
STEGOSAURUS (STEG-OH-SORE-US)

MEANING
ROOF LIZARD

FOOD
MEAT

SIZE
9M

DINO RATING

Give this dinosaur scores out of 10.

FIERCE FACTOR

/10

STRENGTH SCORE

/10

TAIL RATING

/10

SUPER SIZE

The bulky **Stegosaurus** was the same size as which animal? Copy the letters below into the matching coloured circles to find out.

◯ ◯ ◯ ◯ ◯ ◯ ◯ ◯

L E P A E T N H

Answers on pages 48.

PREHISTORIC ADVENTURE

Imagine you're an explorer off on an exciting expedition. Fill in these pages all about your dinosaur discoveries.

1 Before you set off, choose your route on the map.

2 Wow, you've found two fossils. Circle the one that shows a **Triceratops**.

a

b

3 You've uncovered a dinosaur's nest. Count how many eggs are inside.

Answers on pages 48.

4

Look, it's a footprint! Can you identify which dinosaur it belongs to?

Oviraptor

Ankylosaurus

5

Can you see a dinosaur behind the trees? Tick which one it is.

Parasaurolophus

Stegosaurus

6

You've discovered a dinosaur that nobody has ever seen before! Draw a picture of it and give it a name.

ON THE HUNT

Coelophysis had all the ingredients of a successful hunter – speed, fierceness and sharp eyesight. It used these skills to capture insects and small reptiles.

DINO FEAST

Hungry Coelophysis used its sharp claws to grasp and kill prey. It then gobbled up its food with its super sharp teeth. **Ouch!**

IT'S A FACT!

Coelophysis lived in the desert plains of South Africa, the USA and Zimbabwe.

SUPER SPEED

Coelophysis had long legs and a light body so it was a fast runner. It used its long tail to help it balance when running quickly. **Cool!**

COELOPHYSIS

The fast and fierce one.

DINO STATS

NAME
COELOPHYSIS (SEEL-**OH**-FIE-SIS)
MEANING
HOLLOW FORM
FOOD
MEAT
SIZE
3M

DINO RATING

Give this dinosaur scores out of 10.

FIERCE FACTOR

/10

SPEED SCORE

/10

KILLER CLAWS

/10

EGG HUNT

How many Coelophysis eggs can you find hidden on these pages?

DID YOU KNOW?
Coelophysis lived and hunted in packs.

Answers on pages 48.

DINO FOOTPRINT COOKIES

Use your favourite dinosaur toy to help you make these stomping dino footprint cookies. Yum!

INGREDIENTS

Tick the ingredients off as you use them.

 250g butter, softened

 140g caster sugar

 1 egg

 2 tsp vanilla esscence

 300g plain flour

 2-3 tsp ground cinnamon

YOU WILL NEED
- Weighing scales • Sieve
- Wooden spoon • Teaspoon
- Large bowl • Rolling pin
- Circular cookie cutter
- Plastic dinosaur toy, cleaned
- Non-stick baking tray

HOW TO MAKE

 1 Put the butter and sugar in a large bowl and mix them together with a wooden spoon.

 2 Add the egg and vanilla extract and mix them in.

 3 Sift in the flour and mix well.

 4 Using clean hands, press and mix the mixture until it forms a dough.

 5 Pre-heat the oven to 180C/160C fan/gas 4 and chill the dough in the fridge for 30 minutes.

 6 Once chilled, roll the dough out and use a cookie cutter to cut it into shapes.

 7 Mix together 2-3 teaspoons of ground cinnamon with a few drops of water to make a paste and dip in the feet of a clean, plastic dinosaur toy.

ROAR

8 Press the feet onto each cookie to make the footprint indents, being careful not to push too hard though the dough.

9 Bake the cookies on a non-stick baking tray for 10-12 minutes until they're golden.

10 While the cookies are still warm, press the dinosaur feet into the footprint indents again to make them more defined.

11 Leave your cookies to cool. Once cooled, your dino footprint cookies are ready to eat. YUM!

Adult guidance is needed for this activity.

DEADLY WEAPONS

Triceratops used its three sharp horns for fending off attackers or fighting other dinosaurs. Fossils have shown that Triceratops often fought with Tyrannosaurus. Wow!

PROTECTIVE SHIELD

Triceratops had a large, bony frill. It used this eye-catching body part like a shield to protect its neck.

HEFTY DINO

At 9m long, Triceratops was the biggest of all the horned dinosaurs. Its bulky body made it heavy so it couldn't walk very quickly.

DID YOU KNOW?
Triceratops was the last horned dinosaur to walk the Earth.

TRICERATOPS

The one with three horns

DINO STATS

NAME
TRICERATOPS (TRI-**SERRA**-TOPS)

MEANING
THREE-HORNED FACE

FOOD
PLANTS

SIZE
9M

DINO COLOURS

Add some fierce colours to this chunky **Triceratops**.

DINO RATING

Give this dinosaur scores out of 10.

FIERCE FACTOR

/10

SUPER SIZE

/10

HORN RATING

/10

IT'S A FACT!
Triceratops had 800 teeth inside its beak-like mouth.

23

DINO
DIFFERENCES

These two pictures may look the same but don't be fooled, there are eight differences between them. Can you spot them all?

a

Colour a leaf each time you spot a difference.

1 2 3 4

24

Trace over the prehistoric word.

5 6 7 8

UNUSUAL TEETH

Plant-eating Apatosaurus used its spoon-shaped teeth to gather vegetation. This eating machine would have grazed continually throughout the day.

DINO DISCOVERY

An Apatosaurus skeleton was discovered in a quarry in Utah, USA, in 1909. It took the explorer who found it six years to remove the skeleton from the ground.

DID YOU KNOW?
In its hunt for food, Apatosaurus used its long neck to knock down trees.

MOVING HOME

Apatosaurus lived in the USA. It is thought that they migrated in herds like many animals, such as zebras and wildebeest, do today.

MEET THE DINOS
APATOSAURUS
The one with the noisy tail.

DINO STATS

NAME
APATOSAURUS (AH-**PAT**-OH-**SORE**-US)

MEANING
DECEPTIVE LIZARD

FOOD
PLANTS

SIZE
21M

TAIL TIME

Which **Apatosaurus** has the longest tail?

a

b

c

DINO RATING

Give this dinosaur scores out of 10.

FIERCE-FACTOR

/10

SUPER-SIZE

/10

TAIL-SIZE

/10

IT'S A FACT!
Apatosaurus laid eggs as big as basketballs.

Answers on pages 48.

DINOSAUR DETECTIVE

Do you know Velociraptor from Triceratops? Test your dino knowledge by reading the clues below and working out which dinosaurs are being described.

a

CLUE

I walked on two legs. I had tiny arms. I'm known as the dinosaur king.

I am...

SPINOSAURUS

b

CLUE

I had three horns. I had a neck frill. I had a bulky body.

TRICERATOPS

c CLUE

I was the size of a large dog. I could run as fast as a tiger. I had three sharp claws on each hand and foot.

I am...

VELOCIRAPTOR

d CLUE

I was the biggest meat-eating dinosaur. I had crocodile-like teeth. I had an eye-catching sail on my back.

I am...

TYRANNOSAURUS

I am...

TOUGH DINO

Ankylosaurus had thick skin covered in studs that protected its body like armour. This protective shield made the tough dino hard to attack.

BUILT-IN WEAPON

This deadly dino could break attackers' bones with the help of a big club on the end of its tail – a well-aimed swing is all it took to take an enemy down. **Ouch!**

DID YOU KNOW?
Ankylosaurus had small, leaf-shaped teeth.

IT'S A FACT!
Ankylosaurus was wider than it was tall.

SLOW MOVER

Bulky Ankylosaurus walked on four legs. It was a slow-moving dino because of its size and weight, but what it lacked in speed, it made up in strength.

MEET THE DINOS

ANKYLOSAURUS

The one built like a tank.

DINO STATS

NAME	ANKYLOSAURUS (AN-**KIE**-LOH-SORE-US)
MEANING	STIFF LIZARD
FOOD	PLANTS
SIZE	10M

DINO RATING

Give this dinosaur scores out of 10.

FIERCE-FACTOR

/10

STRENGTH SCORE

/10

TAIL RATING

/10

COUNTING FUN

How many **Ankylosaurus** can you count in this dino jumble?

Answers on pages 48.

SUPER SIZES

Wow! Look how tiny humans are compared to some of the dinosaur giants!

SPINOSAURUS

WOW!
Looooong Spinosaurus was bigger than a bus!

WOW!
Ginormous Diplodocus was the size of a blue whale!

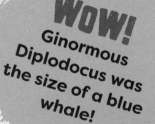

DIPLODOCUS

APATOSAURUS

WOW!
Huge Apatosaurus was nearly the size of a standard swimming pool.

TYRANNOSAURUS

WOW!
T-rex was almost as long as a badminton court.

ALLOSAURUS

WOW!
Allosaurus was the length of four kayaks.

WOW!
Gigantic Ankylosaurus was as long as two cars!

ANKYLOSAURUS

CROC-LIKE DINO

Spinosaurus had long, narrow jaws, a bit like a crocodile's. With its high up nostrils, the dino was perfectly designed for breathing underwater. **Awesome!**

IMPRESSIVE SAIL

Huge Spinosaurus had an enormous sail on its back but scientists don't know for sure what it was for. One idea is that it helped the dinosaur cool down.

FISH HUNTER

As well as meat, hungry Spinosaurus ate fish which it caught in shallow waters. It had webbed feet, like a duck, to help it walk along riverbeds. **Quack quack!**

IT'S A FACT!
Spinosaurus was the longest meat-eating dinosaur.

SPINOSAURUS

The dinosaur with a mysterious sail.

DINO STATS

NAME	SPINOSAURUS (**SPINE**-OH-**SORE**-US)
MEANING	THORN LIZARD
FOOD	MEAT AND FISH
SIZE	16M

DINO RATING

Give this dinosaur scores out of 10.

FIERCE-FACTOR

/10

BIG-BITE

/10

SUPER SAIL

/10

FISH MATCH

Spinosaurus has caught some fish for dinner. Can you match them into pairs?

a
b
c
d
e
f

DID YOU KNOW?

Scientists don't know for certain what a Spinosaurus tail looked like as a whole tail fossil has never been found.

Answers on pages 48.

PIXEL
PICTURE

Use the key to colour the squares the correct colours to reveal this roar-some digi dino.

KEY

| 1 |
| 2 |
| 3 |
| 4 |
| 5 |
| 6 |

```
6 6 6 6 6 6 6 6 6 6 6 6 6 6 6 6 6 6 6 6 6 6 6 6 6 6 6 6 6 6 0 0 0 0
6 6 6 6 6 1 1 6 6 6 6 6 6 6 6 6 6 6 6 6 6 6 6 6 6 6 6 0 0 0 0 0
6 6 6 1 1 2 2 1 1 1 6 6 6 6 6 6 6 6 6 6 6 6 6 6 6 0 0 0 0 0 0 0
6 0 1 2 2 2 2 2 2 1 1 0 0 6 6 6 6 0 0 0 0 0 0 0 0 0 0 0 0 0
0 0 1 1 1 2 2 2 2 2 2 1 0 0 0 0 0 0 0 0 0 0 0 0 0 0 0 0 0 0
0 0 0 0 1 1 2 2 2 2 2 2 1 0 0 0 0 0 0 0 0 0 0 0 0 0 0 0 0
0 0 0 0 0 0 1 1 2 2 2 3 2 1 0 0 0 0 0 0 0 0 0 0 0 0 0 0 0
0 0 0 0 0 0 0 1 2 2 2 2 2 1 0 0 0 0 0 0 0 0 0 0 0 0 0 0
0 1 1 0 0 0 0 0 1 2 2 2 2 2 1 0 0 0 0 0 0 0 0 0 0 0 0 6 6
0 1 2 1 1 1 0 0 1 2 2 2 2 2 1 0 0 0 0 0 0 0 0 0 0 6 6 6
6 6 1 1 2 2 1 1 1 2 2 2 2 2 2 1 0 0 0 0 1 1 1 6 6 6 6
6 6 6 6 1 1 2 2 2 2 2 2 2 2 2 1 0 0 0 0 0 1 2 1 6 6 6
6 6 6 6 6 6 1 1 1 2 2 2 2 2 1 6 0 0 0 6 6 1 2 1 6 6
6 6 6 6 6 6 6 6 1 1 1 2 2 1 6 6 6 6 6 6 1 2 1 6 6
6 6 6 6 6 6 6 6 6 6 6 1 2 2 1 1 1 6 6 6 6 6 1 2 1 6
6 6 6 6 6 6 6 6 6 6 6 1 2 2 1 1 6 6 6 6 6 6 1 2 1 0
6 6 6 6 6 6 6 6 6 1 5 5 1 1 2 1 6 6 6 6 6 1 2 2 1 0
0 0 6 6 6 6 1 1 5 4 4 5 1 2 1 1 1 1 6 1 2 2 1 0
0 0 0 0 6 6 1 2 2 1 4 4 1 2 2 1 2 2 2 1 2 2 2 1 0
0 0 0 0 0 1 2 2 1 4 4 1 2 2 1 2 2 2 2 1 2 2 1 0 0
0 0 0 0 0 1 2 1 1 4 1 2 2 1 2 2 2 2 2 2 1 0 0
0 0 0 0 0 1 1 1 0 1 4 1 2 1 1 2 1 2 2 2 2 1 0 0
6 0 0 0 0 1 0 0 1 4 1 1 1 5 1 2 2 2 2 1 1 0 0 0
6 6 6 0 0 0 0 0 1 1 4 4 1 4 5 1 2 2 2 2 2 1 0 0 0
6 6 6 6 6 0 1 2 2 1 4 4 5 1 2 2 2 2 2 1 0 0 0 6
6 6 6 6 6 6 1 1 2 2 1 5 5 5 1 2 2 2 2 1 0 0 6 6 6
6 6 6 6 6 6 6 1 2 2 2 1 1 1 1 2 2 2 2 1 6 6 6 6
6 6 6 6 6 6 1 2 2 1 6 6 6 1 1 2 2 1 1 6 6 6
6 6 6 6 6 6 1 1 2 2 2 1 6 6 6 1 1 2 2 2 1 6 6
6 6 6 1 1 1 1 2 1 1 2 1 6 6 6 1 1 2 2 2 1 6 6 6
0 6 6 1 2 1 1 2 2 1 6 6 6 1 1 2 1 1 2 1 6 6 6
0 0 0 6 1 1 6 1 1 6 6 6 6 1 1 2 2 1 6 6 6
0 0 0 0 0 6 6 6 6 6 6 6 6 6 6 1 1 6 1 1 1 6 6 6 0
0 0 0 0 0 0 6 6 6 6 6 6 6 6 6 6 6 6 6 6 6 6 0 0
```

JURASSIC JOKES

How do you rate these dinosaur funnies? Are they roar-some or groan-worthy?

What do you call a dinosaur who's a noisy sleeper?
TYRANNO-SNORE-US!

What do you do if you find a dinosaur in your bed?
FIND SOMEWHERE ELSE TO SLEEP!

What's as big as a dinosaur but weighs nothing?
A DINOSAUR'S SHADOW!

What do you call a dinosaur that never gives up?
TRY-TRY-TRY-CERATOPS!

What came after the dinosaur?
IT'S TAIL!

Why can't Tyrannosaurus clap its hands?
BECAUSE IT'S EXTINCT!

RATE IT!

Colour a smiley face or a sad face to rate each joke.

DEADLY BITE

Gigantic Allosaurus had a huge mouth to match its super-size. It was packed full of 70 sharp teeth that curved backwards to stop prey escaping. **Cool!**

IT'S A FACT!

Allosaurus used its long tail to help it balance when it ran.

KILLER CLAWS

Allosaurus had strong, three-fingered hands with razor sharp claws. It used its powerful grip to keep hold of its prey. Ouch!

FIERCE HUNTER

Allosaurus had powerful legs so it could run quickly. Combined with its sharp teeth and claws, this made the massive dino a deadly predator.

MEET THE DINOS

ALLOSAURUS

The king of the North American Jurassic predators.

DINO STATS

NAME
ALLOSAURUS (**AL**-LOH-SAW-US)

MEANING
OTHER LIZARD

FOOD
MEAT

SIZE
12M

DINO RATING

Give this dinosaur scores out of 10.

FIERCE FACTOR

/10

BIG BITE

/10

KILLER CLAWS

/10

FOSSIL FIND

Can you spot this Allosaurus fossil hiding somewhere on these pages?

DID YOU KNOW?
Unlike some dinosaurs, Allosaurus preferred to hunt alone rather than in a pack.

BUILD A DINO

Cut out and create your very own one-of-a-kind dinosaurs and make a roar-some prehistoric picture.

YOU WILL NEED

Scissors   Glue

!

Adult guidance is needed for this activity.

HOW TO MAKE

Make sure you read page 39 before you cut out the shapes. If you don't want to cut up your book, photocopy or scan and print pages 40 and 41 instead.

1. Carefully cut out the shapes below.

2. Have fun arranging the shapes to make different dinosaurs.

3. Once you're happy with your designs, glue your dinosaurs onto the opposite page.

4. Cut out the page along the dotted line and hang your prehistoric picture where everyone can see it. Great job!

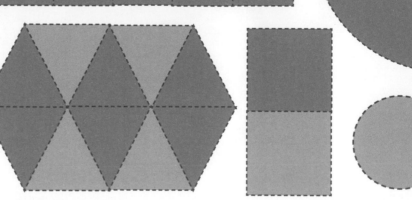

RECORD BREAKER

Supersized Argentinosaurus was the largest animal to ever walk the Earth. Although other dinosaurs were as long and some were taller, Argentinosaurus was the heaviest.

ENORMOUS EGGS

Argentinosaurus laid eggs the size of a football. Scientists have worked out that it would have taken a baby Argentinosaurus about 40 years to grow to full size. **Wow!**

HUNGRY DINO

Argentinosaurus ate a lot of food to fuel its massive body. The gigantic trees it ate from were almost five times taller than the dino. That's big!

DID YOU KNOW?
Heavy Argentinosaurus weighed as much as 20 elephants.

ARGENTINOSAURUS

The huge, heavy one.

DINO STATS

NAME
ARGENTINOSAURUS (**AR**-GENT-EENO-SORE-US)

MEANING
ARGENTINA LIZARD

FOOD
PLANTS

SIZE
35M

DINO RATING

Give this dinosaur scores out of 10.

FIERCE FACTOR

10

SUPER SIZE

10

TAIL-RATING

10

COLOUR SEQUENCE

Colour the white Argentinosaurus footprints the correct colours to repeat the sequence below.

IT'S A FACT!

Argentinosaurus lived in the forests of Argentina 100 million years ago.

Answers on pages 48.

DINO
FIGHT

Were dinosaurs tougher than some of the fiercest animals alive today? You decide by choosing who would win each of these battles.

TYRANNOSAURUS VS **TIGER**

GIGANOTOSAURUS VS **BROWN BEAR**

VELOCIRAPTOR VS **COBRA**

FACT FINDER

Can you crack the code to reveal some roar-some facts about Styracosaurus?

1 The name 'Styracosaurus' means

_ _ _ _ _ _

_ _ _ _ _ _

_

2 Styracosaurus used its

_ _ _ _

_ _ _ _

for fighting.

3

_ _ _ _ _ _ _ _ _ _ _

was Styracosaurus's relative.

Answers on pages 48.

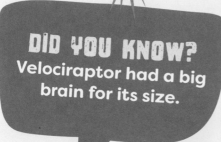

DID YOU KNOW?
Velociraptor had a big brain for its size.

FEEDING TIME

Hungry Velociraptor gobbled up dinosaur eggs, small lizards and small mammals. Experts think it probably ate baby dinosaurs too.

DEADLY WEAPONS

Velociraptor had three pointed claws on each hand and foot, and a mouth full of razor sharp teeth. These built-in weapons made the small dino a vicious predator.

SUPER SPEED

Velociraptor may have been small but it was quick on its feet. This tiny dino could run as fast as a tiger. **Wow!**

MEET THE DINOS

VELOCIRAPTOR

The small, speedy one.

DINO STATS

NAME	
VELOCIRAPTOR (VEL-**OSS**-EE-RAP-TOR)	
MEANING	
SPEED THIEF	
FOOD	
MEAT	
SIZE	
2M	

DINO RATING

Give this dinosaur scores out of 10.

FIERCE-FACTOR

/10

SUPER-SPEED

/10

KILLER CLAWS

/10

TRUE OR FALSE?

Velociraptor had four pointed claws on each hand and foot.

a (TRUE)

b (FALSE)

IT'S A FACT!
Velociraptor was only about the size of a large dog.

Answers on pages 48.

ANSWERS

PAGES 2-3
DINO FOOTPRINTS
10 footprints.

PAGES 4-5
T. REX TRAIL
1. Volcano a is the biggest.
4. Triceratops is hiding behind the boulders.

PAGES 6-7
FINDING FOOD
Dinosaur b.

PAGES 10-11
DINO CLOSE-UPS
a.

PAGE 12
SHADOW MATCH
c.

PAGE 13
FOSSIL FUN

PAGES 14-15
SUPER SIZE
Elephant.

PAGES 16-17
PREHISTORIC ADVENTURE
2. Fossil a shows Triceratops.
3. There are 6 eggs.
4. The footprint belongs to Ankylosaurus.
5. The dinosaur behind the tree is Stegosaurus.

PAGES 18-19
EGG HUNT
6 eggs.

PAGES 24-25
DINO DIFFERENCES

PAGES 26-27
TAIL TIME
b.

PAGES 28-29
DINOSAUR DETECTIVE
A – Tyrannosaurus
B – Triceratops
C – Velociraptor
D – Spinosaurus

PAGES 30-31
COUNTING FUN
6 Ankylosaurus.

PAGES 34-35
FISH MATCH
a and d, b and e, c and f.

PAGES 42-43
COLOUR SEQUENCE

PAGE 45
FACT FINDER
1. Spiked Lizard.
2. Nose horn.
3. Triceratops.

PAGES 46-47
TRUE OR FALSE?
Velociraptor had three pointed claws on each hand and foot.